Hello, my name is:

_____ ,

(your signature)

BIG NATE'S #1 FAN

D0865488

Lincoln Peirce

BiG NATE

FUN BLASTER

HarperCollins *Children's Books*

First published in Great Britain by HarperCollins *Children's Books* in 2012
HarperCollins *Children's Books* is a division of HarperCollins*Publishers* Ltd,
77-85 Fulham Palace Road, Hammersmith, London, W6 8JB.

The HarperCollins website address is:
www.harpercollins.co.uk

1

Text and illustration copyright © 2012 United Feature Syndicate, Inc.

ISBN 978-0-00-745713-7

The author asserts the moral right to be identified
as the author of this work.

Printed and bound in England by
Clays Ltd, St Ives plc

MIX
Paper from
responsible sources
FSC   FSC C007454
www.fsc.org

FSC™ is a non-profit international organisation established to promote
the responsible management of the world's forests. Products carrying the
FSC label are independently certified to assure consumers that they come
from forests that are managed to meet the social, economic and
ecological needs of present and future generations,
and other controlled sources.

Find out more about HarperCollins and the environment at
www.harpercollins.co.uk/green

For Big Nate Fans Everywhere –
Especially if you love
Nicknames,
Scribbling,
Secret codes,
Cartoons, and
Pop quizzes (OK, forget that last one)

HOW WELL DO U KNOW NATE?

Do you surpass all others
when it comes to Nate trivia? Test it out!

1. Nate's had it with Randy the bully. How does he get his revenge?

a. Beating him at dodgeball

b. Eating all his Cheez Doodles

c. Making him eat 10 lemon squares in a row

d. Throwing a pie in his face

e. Stealing his girlfriend

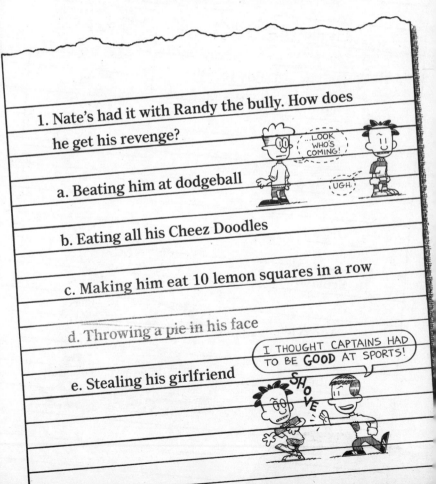

2. Nate became friends with Teddy when...

a. They joined the same fleeceball team.

b. Teddy gave Nate his egg rolls at lunch.

c. Teddy pretended his science lab squid was a booger.

d. Teddy moved next door.

SESAME CHICKEN, SPARERIBS, A COUPLE OF EGG ROLLS...

e. Nate invited Teddy to join
his band, Enslave the Mollusk.

3. Nate's sign

a. Virgo

WHAT'S YOUR SIGN?

b. Scorpio

c. Aquarius

d. Libra

e. Capricorn

4. Nate's superhero self is called…

a. Super Nate

b. Mr Magnificent

c. Wonder Kid

d. Ultra-Nate

e. Nate the Notorious

5. Nate wanted his fleeceball team to have this name:

a. Killer Bees

b. Pumas

c. Chargers

d. Raptors

e. Psycho Dogs

CODE CRACKER

Go undercover and help solve the secret messages using this code. Then circle whether they are true or false.

SOMETIMES MY BRILLIANCE SURPRISES EVEN **ME**!

Don't lose this SECRET CODE!

⊕ = A	⊕ = J	⊕ = R
⊕ = B	⊕ = K	⊕ = S
⊕ = C	⊕ = L	⊕ = T
⊕ = D	⊕ = M	⊕ = U
⊕ = E	⊕ = N	⊕ = V
⊕ = F	⊕ = O	⊕ = W
⊕ = G	⊕ = P	⊕ = X
⊕ = H	⊕ = Q	⊕ = Y
⊕ = I		⊕ = Z

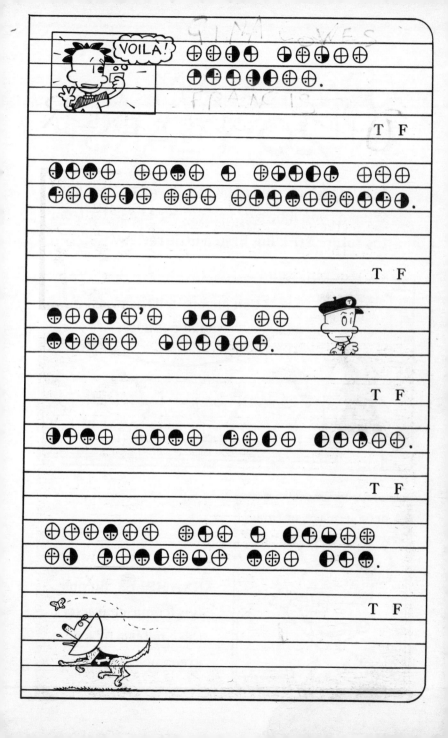

WHO AM I IN **20** YEARS?

Imagine what you will be like 20 years from now! Whoa… you'll be a grown-up! Write a letter from the future YOU. But first, a little review…

Can anyone tell the class what a noun is?

A person, place, or thing!

EXAMPLES: Bumble Boy (comic character), the cafeteria (place), green bean (thing)

EXAMPLES:
doodle, paint, compete, yell

EXAMPLES:
amazing (describes Pickles),
smart (describes Artur),
terrifying (describes Mrs Godfrey)

An adverb describes a verb!

**AN EXAMPLE OF AN
ADVERB IN A SENTENCE:**
Francis and Teddy think Nate
behaves *weirdly* around Jenny.

YOU'RE SUCH A **SLOB**!

JENNY!

WHAT ARE YOU WRITING?

NOTHING! **NOTHING!**

IT LOOKS LIKE A LETTER.

OK, **OK**! I'LL **TELL** YOU!

NOW MAKE A LIST OF WORDS ALL ABOUT YOU!

1. Your name:

2. Adjective:

3. Noun:

4. Adjective:

5. Adverb:

6. Verb:

7. Verb:

8. Noun:

9. Verb:

10. Plural noun:

11. Verb:

12. Plural noun:

13. Adjective:

14. Noun:

15. Noun:

16. Noun (place name):

17. Plural noun:

18. Plural noun:

19. Adverb:

20. Noun:

TURN THE PAGE AND USE YOUR LIST
TO FILL IN THE BLANKS!

Dear _____ ,
       1.

My life is pretty _____ because I work as a
                      2.

_____ , which I find extremely _____ .
    3.   4.

After work I _____ _____ and
                  5.   6.

_____ . Every day is an _____ because
     7.   8.

I _____ _____ and _____ .
    9.   10.   11.

I think _____ should make a reality show
              12.

all about my _____ _____ . I live in
                    13.   14.

a _____ in the country of _____ ,
       15.   16.

with _____ and _____ . My
          17.   18.

most exciting moment ever was when I _____
                                          19.

climbed _____ !!
              20.

DOODLE CRAZE

Do you go crazy when you doodle? Well, what are you waiting for? Start by signing your name in crazy ways, just like Nate does here.

Nate Wright
Nate Wright
Nate Wright

WHAT A **SAVE!**

SCOUT'S HONOUR

How many badges can Nate's troop earn? See if you can guess these merit badge activities!

ACROSS

1. Sing it, dance to it, or buy it for your iPod.

3. Mmmm, grilling hot dogs over the fire and making baked beans – better put on your apron for this.

6. Breaststroke, backstroke, butterfly – what is this?

8. Something you mold with clay. Rhymes with "vulture".

9. You'll need oars for this. Rhymes with "snowing". Don't get swept away in the current!

10. Draw! Paint! Create! You'll need your easel for this activity.

11. Take bait and a pole!

13. It rains, it snows, it's sunny or dry! What is this called?

14. The trees, the earth, Mother _____ .

DOWN

2. Don't forget your sleeping bag and tent.

4. If you have a green thumb, then you're very good at this!

5. What kit holds plasters?

7. Build a birdhouse, get a badge in _____ing. First syllable rhymes with "could".

12. This can be done on ice or on concrete, and you'll need special shoes.

MOST VALUABLE PLAYER

Who made the game-winning save?
Solve the maze and find out.

SEMAPHORE SUPERSTAR

Nate invented a special semaphore code so that he and his friends Teddy and Francis can send secret messages that no one else can read – except you! Decode their first message below.

CODE CHART Use this alphabet to decode the secret messages in this book!

▪=A	=E	=I	=M	=Q	=W
=B	=F	=J	=N	=R	=X
=C	=G	=K	=O	=S	=Y
=D	=H	=L	=P	=T	=Z
			=U		
			=V		

UN-YUMMY TREATS

Nate loves Cheez Doodles, but his house is a no-snack zone! Help him avoid these gross foods by filling in the blanks so only one of each food appears in every row, column and box.

UNHAPPY EATING!

NATE WRIGHT, FOOD CRITIC

SUPER SCRIBBLE GAME

Turn your super scribble into...

Don't forget to write a caption for it:

IT'S SHOWTIME!

You're in the spotlight! Guess the clues and take the lead. If you haven't memorised the semaphore code, use the chart on page 15.

◎🔲🔳◆ ▮🔲🔳◼ ▽🔳 ▽◆?

SOLVE THE PUZZLE AND FIND OUT!

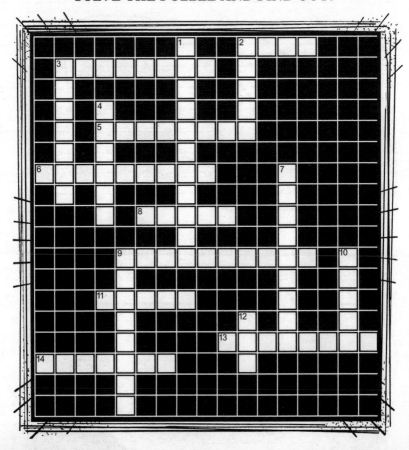

ACROSS

2. Seen in the the night sky, or as the lead in a play.

3. The boy who flies!

5. Many hands clapping for the performers at the end of the play.

6. A faraway magical place where people don't grow old.

8. Weapon that is long and sharp.

9. Rhymes with "wink her tell".

11. She follows her brothers out the window and into the night sky.

13. These are the young men who will never grow up.

14. Usually red cloth, this lifts and drops to mark the beginning and end of the show.

DOWN

1. His hand was eaten by a crocodile.

2. Where all the action in a play happens.

3. They wear eye patches and plunder ships.

4. Actors wear this on their faces so their features can be seen from far away.

7. Shines brightly in a circle on the stage. Nate loves this!

9. On a ship, you must walk _____ _____ if you're found to be an enemy.

10. A tiny creature with wings.

12. Take a _____ . Rhymes with "cow".

GINA SAYS, NATE SAYS

It's no secret that Nate and Gina are all-time enemies! Whatever Gina says, Nate thinks the opposite, like this:

NOW YOU TRY GUESSING WHAT NATE WOULD SAY!

FAST AND FURIOUS FLEECEBALL

Get ready to play ball! Using the letters that spell Nate's favorite SPOFF, let's see if you can create more than 20 other words!

FLEECEBALL

1. Lab	12.
2.	13.
3.	14.
4.	15.
5.	16.
6.	17.
7.	18.
8.	19.
9.	20.
10.	21.
11.	22.

YES! I'M A FLEECE-BALL CAPTAIN!!

HEADLINERS

Extra, extra, read all about it! Pretend you're a
reporter and write a headline for each scene.

_____

_____

_____

_____

_____

_____

CLASSROOM CHATTER

Nate's got lots of talents, but he's especially skilled at eavesdropping! He writes the gossip column for the school paper. It's called Classroom Chatter! How does he get the best scoop? From hanging out in front of the teachers' lounge!

On pages 6–8, Ms Clarke refreshed your memory about the parts of speech.

WRITE THE MOST GOSSIPY WORDS
YOU CAN THINK OF!

1. Noun (person):

2. Adjective:

3. Noun (plural):

4. Noun (person):

5. Noun (person):

6. Noun (person):

7. Adjective:

8. Noun:

9. Verb (ending in -ing):

10. Verb (ending in -ing):

11. Noun (person):

12. Noun:

13. Noun:

14. Noun (person):

15. Adjective:

16. Noun:

**TURN THE
PAGE TO GET
THE SCOOP!**

BLUSH!

OH, MY!

EXCLUSIVE NEWS!
YOU HEARD
IT HERE FIRST!

_____ was seen throwing _____
1.   2.

_____ with _____ near
3.   4.

_____ 's locker after school.
5.

_____ was seen throwing _____
6.   7.

_____ and secretly _____ after
8.   9.

publicly _____ at recess.
10.

Will _____ have a change of _____?
11.   12.

Or is the _____ over for good?
13.

Only _____ knows the _____
14.   15.

_____ .
16.

HIKE TO NOWHERE

What awaits Nate at the end of his hike? Solve the maze and find out!

START

FSSSST! FINISH

TIMBER SCOUTS

Nate, Teddy, and Francis are Timber Scouts. Now they need to make room for... Artur! Make sure each boy's initial appears only once in every row, column, and box.

  = **NATE**

 = **TEDDY**

 = **FRANCIS**

  = **ARTUR**

F		T	
	N	A	
	T	F	
A			

TIME TO RHYME

Nate likes to rhyme,
more than mime,
all of the time!

Create pairs of
rhyming words
that match these
funny definitions.

He's in an imaginary box!

GET AN IMAGINARY LIFE!

Mime

EXAMPLES:

1. Extra large feline   <u>fat</u>   <u>cat</u>

2. Rodent dwelling   <u>mouse</u>   <u>house</u>

LICK LICK LICK
SLURP SLUP SLURP
LICK   LICK
SLOP
SLUP

NOW YOU TRY!

3. Silly rabbit   _____   _____

4. Peaceful mother   calm   ___

5. Angry father   ____   ___

6. Wacky white-petalled
    flower   _____   _____

7. Weird ape   funky   _____

8. Reading corner   ____   nook

9. Not the right tune   _____   ____

10. Pleasure-filled race   fun   ___

ARTUR IS PERFECT, PEOPLE SAY, BUT I JUST WISH HE'D GO AWAY.

TEDDY'S ULTIMATE SPORTS TRIVIA

Teddy is wild about sports. Can you decode his secret messages?

A	B	C	D	E	F	G	H	I	J	K	L	M
Z	Y	X	W	V	U	T	S	R	Q	P	O	N

N	O	P	Q	R	S	T	U	V	W	X	Y	Z
M	L	K	J	I	H	G	F	E	D	C	B	A

H S Z J F R O O V L M V Z O

D V Z I H   G S V   O Z I T V H G

H S L V H   R M   G S V   M Y Z

22!

H R A V

G S V   G L F I   W V   U I Z M X V

Y R X B X O V   I Z X V

O Z H G H **21**   W Z B H '   Z M W

O Z M X V   Z I N H G I L M T

S Z H   D L M   Z   I V X L I W

7 G R N V H !

SUPER SCRIBBLE GAME

Ready. Set. Scribble!

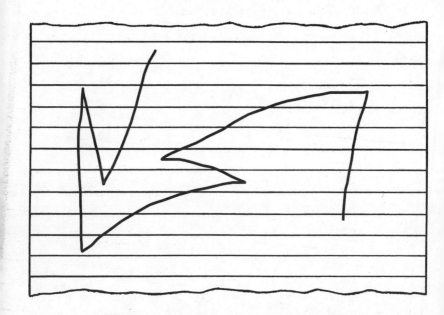

Don't forget to write a caption for it:

FRIENDS FOREVER

Nate's super tight with his buddies Francis and Teddy! Who are your favorite amigos?

NAME THE FRIEND MOST LIKELY TO…

Talk in a Donald Duck voice _____

Wear a wild-looking hat to school _____

Eat buttered popcorn-flavor jelly beans _____

Do a handstand in Social Studies _____

Make up a new song _____

Laugh so it sounds like a goose _____

Do jumping jacks every day _____

Try out for the football team _____

Recite lines from a favourite book _____

Get an A in science class _____

Draw comics featuring
out-of-this-world characters _____

Take the team to victory in kickball _____

CAMPER DAD COMIX

Why is Nate's dad so clueless? Fill in the speech bubbles and create your own comix.

DOG DAZE

Nate thinks his neighbor's dog, Spitsy, is pretty cool... if you ignore the fact that Spitsy wears a goofy-looking dog sweater!

What kind of dogs do you love?
See if you can find all the different dogs in this hidden word puzzle!

BASSET HOUND

BEAGLE

BULLDOG

CHIHUAHUA

COCKER SPANIEL

DALMATIAN

GOLDEN RETRIEVER

GREYHOUND

IRISH SETTER

LABRADOR

MALTESE

NEWFOUNDLAND

POMERANIAN

POODLE

PUG

SAINT BERNARD

SCOTTISH TERRIER

```
R G B D N N B R O R U E E P L A R
E L E I N A P S R E K C O C I A I
V U A D R Y O U T I S M A T N N R
E R G S P D G S G R E Y H O U N D
I S L P O L N E C R S E R E D D D
R N E N O G D U A E G A A A E R D
T I N T D T T N O T U O B H A N B
E U A N L E I H A H R L D N A A B
R L I O E A E H A S T E R L I R W
N A T E N C M U L I R E D A L I E
E B A P H R H N N T B N S I I U N
D R M R O I Y E H T U L S S L N B
L A L I H E T N N O E D E N A O L
O D A C G O D I F C A D I T A B R
G O D B R T A W E S E I U D E O P
I R I S H S E T T E R P N U L D P
U A I M S N E O N T D H A R I E D
```

HOW DOES THAT SOUND, SPITSY?

WURF!

YOU'LL HELP ME THINK OF SOMETHING, RIGHT?

WUFF!

SPITSY, CHAMPION DOG

WOW! THEY NOW HAVE A **DNA TEST** FOR MUTTS TO FIGURE OUT EXACTLY WHAT COMBINATION OF BREEDS THEY ARE!

WORF!

WE SHOULD DO THAT FOR **YOU**, SPITSY! YOU COULD BE PART COLLIE, PART DOBERMAN, PART **ANYTHING**!

PANT PANT PANT PANT

YOU COULD HAVE THE BLOODLINES OF A **CHAMPION**! YOU MIGHT VERY WELL HAVE DESCENDED FROM **CANINE ROYALTY**!

SPITSY?

HE'S EATING CAT POOP AGAIN.

© 2009 by NEA, Inc.

COMIX GENIUS

What is the name for a comics genius? A cartoonist, of course! Turn on your genius and see if you can make more than 20 other words with these letters!

CARTOONIST

1.	12.
2.	13.
3.	14.
4.	15.
5.	16.
6.	17.
7.	18.
8.	19.
9.	20.
10.	21.
11.	22.

BECAUSE BEN FRANKLIN WAS A CARTOONIST HIMSELF!

EXACTLY!

EW!

PAT PAT

BREAKFAST BOOK CLUB

At BBC, Breakfast Book Club, the kids at P.S. 38 talk about books!

List the most memorable books you've read. Then grade them from A to F!

BOOK TITLE	GRADE
1.	___
2.	___
3. *Big Nate: The Boy with the Biggest Head in the World*	A
4.	___
5.	___
6. *Big Nate Strikes Again*	A
7.	___
8.	___
9. *Big Nate on a Roll*	A
10.	___
11.	___
12. *Big Nate Goes for Broke*	A

DOOR-TO-DOOR DISASTERS!

Nate has had some unfortunate door-to-door selling encounters. Fill in the blanks so that each letter shows up once in every box, row and column.

W = **WARM FUZZIES**

P = **WRAPPING PAPER**

C = **CANDY BARS**

S = **SCENTED CANDLES**

M = **MAGAZINE SUBSCRIPTIONS**

R = **RAFFLE TICKETS**

This was the worst! Decode the message on page 47 to find out why.

INVENTION CONVENTION

Nate is super creative when he's making things up, like excuses when he hasn't finished his homework, teacher nicknames, or funny new inventions, like the Belsh! Now it's your turn to invent!

WATCH + PEN = _____

SCARF + HAT = _____

CAMERA + GLASSES = _____

FLIP-FLOPS + FAN = _____

UMBRELLA + _____ = _____

BALL + _____ = _____

_____ + _____ = _____

_____ + _____ = _____

AHEM! "THANKS TO **NATE'S** CREATIVITY!"

THAT'S A QUOTE FROM MRS GODFREY, BY THE WAY!

LAUGH RIOT

Teddy's a jokester. Decode (see page 34) his favorite jokes!

Q: ___ ___ ___ _____ _____ ___ ____?

D S B   W R W   G S V   Y L L T V I   X I L H H   G S V   I L Z W

A: _____ __ ___ _____ _____ __!

Y V X Z F H V   S V   D Z H   Y V R M T   K R X P V W   L M

LIFE WITH ELLEN

Look at Nate as a little kid! This is how Nate remembers his big sister, Ellen. Now pretend you're Ellen and tell the same story from HER point of view.

Me and Ellen

Need help with definitions of the parts of speech? Visit Ms Clarke's class on pages 6–8.

MAKE A LIST OF WORDS
THAT ELLEN WOULD USE!

1. Noun: 7. Verb:

2. Verb (ending in -ing):   8. Adverb:

3. Noun: 9. Verb:

4. Noun: 10. Noun:

5. Adverb: 11. Noun:

6. Adjective: 12. Noun:

WE'RE GETTING BACK OUR
BOOK REPORTS, WHICH I
KNOW I DID WELL ON!
AND I'M TRYING OUT FOR
THE SCHOOL MUSICAL!
AND I'M RUNNING FOR
CLASS PRESIDENT! AND
THEN ___ING TO WORK
ON A ___ TINE ___ AT
CHEE___ NG PRA___ SO
TOE R___ THE GIR___ BUT
W HAV___ T DECIDED ___ I'M
C___ ___ ABOUT ___ T ___ EN
___ ___ SUPER F___ ___ S
___ HEN

TURN THE PAGE TO READ

ELLEN'S SIDE OF THE STORY!

When Nate was a _____ , he was always
                        1.

_____ around the _____
        2.   3.

and spitting up _____ . I was a
                        4.

_____ _____ big sister and
        5.   6.

taught him how to _____ _____
                        7.   8.

and _____ . Deep down, he knows
        9.

I am a _____ , because it's obvious I'm
            10.

a super _____ . Too bad he's a little
                11.

_____ !
    12.

MAKE A LIST OF WORDS
THAT ELLEN WOULD USE!

1. Noun:

7. Verb:

2. Verb (ending in -ing):

8. Adverb:

3. Noun:

9. Verb:

4. Noun:

10. Noun:

5. Adverb:

11. Noun:

6. Adjective:

12. Noun:

_____ !
12.

ALL-STAR CARDS

Become an all-star athlete – draw your very own trading card featuring YOU!

LATER, SKATER

Nate is one super skateboarder. But there's one thing he wants most of all – his own customised skateboard!

DESIGN YOUR DREAM SKATEBOARD!

FRANCIS'S CLASSIFIED CODE

No one will ever guess my code!

What number should F be?

Francis made his own secret alphabet. But Nate can decode Francis's messages... and so can you!

A	B	C	D	E	F	G	H	I	J	K	L	M
13	7	26	25	8	16	3	1	20	4	12	23	18

N	O	P	Q	R	S	T	U	V	W	X	Y	Z
21	11	2	15	14	24	6	10	19	22	17	9	5

I know I can figure it out!

$\overline{24}\ \overline{26}\ \overline{20}\ \overline{8}\ \overline{21}\ \overline{6}\ \overline{20}\ \overline{24}\ \overline{6}\ \overline{24}$

$\overline{20}\ \overline{21}\quad \overline{2}\ \overline{8}\ \overline{14}\ \overline{10}$

$\overline{16}\ \overline{11}\ \overline{10}\ \overline{21}\ \overline{25}\quad \overline{13}\quad \overline{3}\ \overline{20}\ \overline{13}\ \overline{21}\ \overline{6}$

$\overline{2}\ \overline{8}\ \overline{21}\ \overline{3}\ \overline{10}\ \overline{20}\ \overline{21}\quad \overline{6}\ \overline{1}\ \overline{13}\ \overline{6}$

$\overline{23}\ \overline{20}\ \overline{19}\ \overline{8}\ \overline{25}\quad \overline{6}\ \overline{1}\ \overline{20}\ \overline{14}\ \overline{6}\ \overline{9}\ \overline{}$

$\overline{24}\ \overline{20}\ \overline{17}\quad \overline{18}\ \overline{20}\ \overline{23}\ \overline{23}\ \overline{20}\ \overline{11}\ \overline{21}$

$\overline{9}\ \overline{8}\ \overline{13}\ \overline{14}\ \overline{24}\quad \overline{13}\ \overline{3}\ \overline{11}\ .$

BADGE BONANZA

How many Timber Scout merit badges does Nate have? Fill in the blank squares so each badge letter appears once in every column, row and box.

(F) = **FITNESS BADGE**

(H) = **HELPING HANDS BADGE**

(C) = **ARTS & CRAFTS BADGE**

(A) = **FIRST AID BADGE**

Nutrition (because I'd have to give up Cheez Doodles), Bugling, Taxidermy, Sewing, Tap Dancing

NAME THAT GNOME

Nate has one VERY odd job – moving garden gnomes! See if you can come up with more than 10 funny gnome names!

1.	11. Jolly Wally
2.	12.
3.	13.
4.	14.
5. Funny Face	15.
6.	16.
7.	17.
8.	18.
9.	19.
10.	20.

BONUS ROUND: Speaking of little guys, can you name all the dwarfs from Snow White?

1. H _ _ _ _
2. B _ _ _ _ _ _
3. G _ _ _ _ _
4. Doc
5. Sleepy
6. D _ _ _ _
7. S _ _ _ _ _

HAPPY HAIKU

Nate's quite a poet. How about you? Nate even writes haiku!

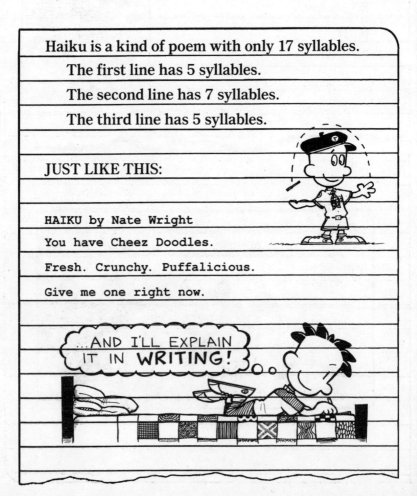

Haiku is a kind of poem with only 17 syllables.

The first line has 5 syllables.

The second line has 7 syllables.

The third line has 5 syllables.

JUST LIKE THIS:

HAIKU by Nate Wright

You have Cheez Doodles.

Fresh. Crunchy. Puffalicious.

Give me one right now.

...AND I'LL EXPLAIN IT IN **WRITING!**

HERE'S ANOTHER HAIKU:

Nate's locker smells gross,

Like Cheez Doodles and gym socks.

Papers falling out.

IF YOU ARE **CLEAN** YOUR LOCKER, IT WILL MAYBE NOT BE SO **MESSY!**

NOW YOU TRY!

1. **Detention again.**

2. _____

3. _____

1. **Gina gets an A.**

2. _____

3. _____

1. **The nickname czar rules.**

2. _____

3. _____

ALIAS

Nate has many different nicknames for Mrs Godfrey, his horrifying social studies teacher. Fill in the blanks so only one of each Godfrey alias appears in every row, column and box.

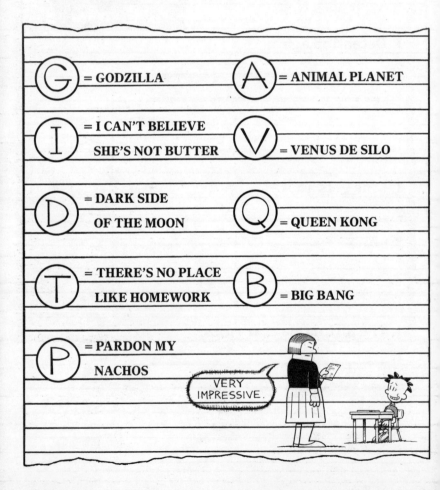

G = GODZILLA

A = ANIMAL PLANET

I = I CAN'T BELIEVE SHE'S NOT BUTTER

V = VENUS DE SILO

D = DARK SIDE OF THE MOON

Q = QUEEN KONG

T = THERE'S NO PLACE LIKE HOMEWORK

B = BIG BANG

P = PARDON MY NACHOS

VERY IMPRESSIVE.

G	B	T		Q	I	D	A	
		A			B	I		
I		V	G	D			Q	
B	V		I					Q
		G	Q		V	B	D	T
T		Q	D		P	G		I
D		I	V		Q	P	B	
V			A		G	Q	I	D
A		P				V		G

SUPER SCOUT CHALLENGE

Being a scout means rising to the challenge! Just ask Nate. See if you can find all the key scouting words in the puzzle.

MARSHMALLOW

TROOP

FORT

CLIMBING

HIKING

SURVIVAL

OATH

CAMPFIRE

BADGES

UNIFORM

WALKING STICK

ARCHERY

SLEEPING BAG

CABINS

HANDSHAKE

FRIENDSHIP

OUTDOORS

G H C G I O I B R O C G H
N A A S I I A L C H M D P
I N B B R D I A T P R W K
K D I G G O M A I E O P C
I S N E N P O H H L F L L
H H S S F I S D L O I C P
A A U I M D P A T M N C O
R K R L N N M E B U U O O
R E V E A H W I E O O P R
K C I T S G N I K L A W T
R R V R S G T N Y I S R R
F K A R C H E R Y A O O G
S M L G T L A A E F B N N

JUST TELL ME WHAT HAPPENED DURING THE TROOP MEETING.

YOU ARE THE INVENTOR

What new thing would you invent?

Draw it!

BACKPACK / SNACK DISPENCER

HEADBAND / FAN

MAKE UP YOUR OWN WACKY INVENTION!

OPEN FOR BUSINESS

Nate is the master of all jobs, big and small! Name 20 jobs where you shine!

1. _____
2. _____
3. _____
4. _____
5. Selling cookies _____
6. _____
7. _____
8. _____
9. _____

YAAAAAH!

10. ___Walking the dog___

11. _____

12. _____

13. _____

14. ___Making comic books___

15. _____

16. _____

17. _____

18. _____

19. _____

20. _____

COVER CRAZE

Are you an artist extraordinaire or a daring designer? Check out these cool covers!

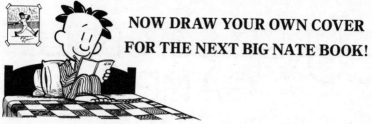

NOW DRAW YOUR OWN COVER FOR THE NEXT BIG NATE BOOK!

SUPER SCRIBBLE GAME

Got nothing to do? It must be scribble game time!

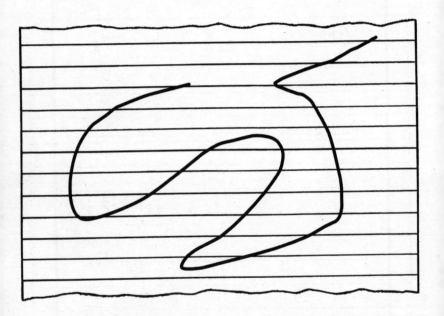

Don't forget to write a caption for it:

WHAT'S ANNOYING?

What's super annoying? List 10 things that make you crazy.

1. Stepping on gum

2. Bad haircut

3. Eating peas

4.

5.

6.

7.

8.

9.

10.

FAR-OUT FACTOIDS

Francis is a serious fan of factoids. Can you decode these wacky facts using Francis's secret code on page 58?

$\overline{1}$ $\overline{10}$ $\overline{18}$ $\overline{13}$ $\overline{21}$ $\overline{24}$

$\overline{1}$ $\overline{13}$ $\overline{19}$ $\overline{8}$

$\overline{11}$ $\overline{19}$ $\overline{8}$ $\overline{14}$

$\overline{24}$ $\overline{8}$ $\overline{19}$ $\overline{8}$ $\overline{21}$ $\overline{6}$ $\overline{1}$ $\overline{11}$ $\overline{10}$ $\overline{24}$ $\overline{13}$ $\overline{21}$ $\overline{25}$

$\overline{25}$ $\overline{20}$ $\overline{16}$ $\overline{16}$ $\overline{8}$ $\overline{14}$ $\overline{8}$ $\overline{21}$ $\overline{6}$

$\overline{16}$ $\overline{13}$ $\overline{26}$ $\overline{20}$ $\overline{13}$ $\overline{23}$

$\overline{8}$ $\overline{17}$ $\overline{2}$ $\overline{14}$ $\overline{8}$ $\overline{24}$ $\overline{24}$ $\overline{20}$ $\overline{11}$ $\overline{21}$ $\overline{24}$.

$\overline{20}\ \overline{21}$ $\overline{13}\ \overline{21}$ $\overline{13}\ \overline{19}\ \overline{8}\ \overline{14}\ \overline{13}\ \overline{3}\ \overline{8}$

$\overline{23}\ \overline{20}\ \overline{16}\ \overline{8}\ \overline{6}\ \overline{20}\ \overline{18}\ \overline{8}$, $\overline{9}\ \overline{11}\ \overline{10}$

$\overline{22}\ \overline{20}\ \overline{23}\ \overline{23}$ $\overline{7}\ \overline{14}\ \overline{8}\ \overline{13}\ \overline{6}\ \overline{1}\ \overline{8}$

$\overline{13}\ \overline{14}\ \overline{11}\ \overline{10}\ \overline{21}\ \overline{25}$ $\overline{24}\ \overline{20}\ \overline{17}$

$\overline{1}\ \overline{10}\ \overline{21}\ \overline{25}\ \overline{14}\ \overline{8}\ \overline{25}$

$\overline{18}\ \overline{20}\ \overline{23}\ \overline{23}\ \overline{20}\ \overline{11}\ \overline{21}$

$\overline{7}\ \overline{14}\ \overline{8}\ \overline{13}\ \overline{6}\ \overline{1}\ \overline{24}$.

ON THE GEOLOGIC TIME SCALE, WHAT EPOCH FALLS BETWEEN THE PALEOCENE AND THE OLIGOCENE?

GYM IS A DISASTER

Nate once had to run wind sprints with his stomach full of green beans, in shorts that were way too big. Talk about uncomfortable! Name your biggest gym disasters.

1.

2.

3.

4.

5. Watching your crush be assigned to the other team

6.

7.

8.

9. Climbing the rope to the ceiling and having
   to pee SO bad!

10.

11.

12.

13.

14.

15. Facing down the school bully in dodgeball

I THOUGHT CAPTAINS HAD TO BE **GOOD** AT SPORTS!

HEH HEH

YEAH, RANDY!

HA HA

HA HA

SHOVE

NOW WHAT HAPPENS? YOU DECIDE!

MAD FOR BADGES

Nate does cool things to earn his merit badges. Check out his sharp Timber Scouts uniform!

DESIGN YOUR OWN MERIT BADGES
FOR EACH ACTIVITY!

WILDERNESS SURVIVAL

MUSIC

ASTRONOMY

COOKING

X-TREME SPORTS

SCRIBBLE BREAK

Take a breather and turn this scribble
into a masterpiece!

Don't forget the caption!

RHYME-A-THON

Are you a rhyming champ like Nate? Decide which pairs of rhyming words will match the funny clues.

1. Group of friends you just met

_ _ _ _ _ _ _ crew

2. Royal leader's finger jewellery

_ _ _ _ _ _'s _ _ _ _ _

3. Quiet and bashful man

_ _ _ _ shy _ _ _ _

4. Super 6th grader who likes Cheez Doodles

_ _ _ _ great _ _ _ _ _

5. Beautiful cat

_ _ _ _ _ _ _ _ _ _ _ _ _

6. Circus performer's city

clown's _ _ _ _ _

7. Gloomy opposite of night

grey _ _ _ _

8. Not heavy, a toy you can fly in the sky

_ _ _ _ _ _ _ kite

9. This black bird doesn't move fast

_ _ _ _ _ _ _ _ _

10. A very large hog

_ _ _ _ _ _ pig

There once was a fellow named Nate,
Who was king of P.S. 38.
Then Artur moved to town.
Now he's stealing Nate's crown.
How come everyone thinks **HE'S** so great?

CREATE-A-COMIX!

Pick up your pencil and let your imagination run wild! Create a comic using Nate, green beans and Teddy.

YOUR TITLE HERE

SKATER SCRAMBLE

Dude! Nate can skate. He's got wicked cool moves!
Now let's see what you can do. Using the letters
in "skateboard", see how many words you can
create!

SKATEBOARD

1.	11.
2.	12.
3.	13.
4.	14.
5.	15.
6.	16.
7.	17.
8.	18.
9.	19.
10.	20.

TOP **5** DOGGONE FACTS

Nate's neighbour's dog, Spitsy, is a little bit strange!
Fill in the rest of these funny facts.

1 He likes CATS!!!

2 He watches lame TV shows
with _____.

3 He gets bullied by _____.

4 Instead of playing fetch, he
prefers to play _____.

5 He wears a
purple sweater
all the time
because he
thinks it makes
him look like
a canine
supermodel.

Rowr!

HOW ABOUT YOUR PET? LIST HIS OR HER
WILD AND WACKY FACTS HERE!

1.   11.

2.   12.

3. Drinks out of the toilet   13.

4.   14.

5.   15. Rubs his face on
                                            everything

6.   16.

7.   17.

8.   18.

9.   19. Eats daisies

10.   20.

MY BEST FRIEND IS A SPORTS CHAMP

Create a player card that stars your best friend!
Name the sport! Name the team!

DOODLE 'ROUND THE CLOCK

Fill this page with doodles!

DRAMATIC FLASHBACK!

What happened before? You decide and draw it!

HOW DID NATE GET A BLACK EYE?

⊞ ⊡ ⬚ ▭ ! _____

WHY DID SPITSY GO CRAZY?

WHY IS NATE IN TROUBLE AGAIN?

□■-⊞■! _____

IS NATE GOING TO THE
PRINCIPAL'S OFFICE? WHY?

THE FORTUNE-TELLER

Nate loves knowing his fortune, even if it means eating too many fortune cookies! Nate just went to Pu Pu Panda – help him decode all of his fortunes.

RAGE-O-METER

What drives you crazy? How do these rank on your RAGE-O-METER?

1. You have to leave your friend's birthday party early.

☐ MIFFED   ☐ HACKED OFF

☐ MAD   ☐ BALLISTIC

RAGE-O-METER

MIFFED • MAD • HACKED OFF • BALLISTIC

2. Your dad is snoring super loud during your favourite movie.

☐ MIFFED   ☐ HACKED OFF

☐ MAD   ☐ BALLISTIC

3. You lose your lucky hat.

☐ MIFFED   ☐ HACKED OFF

☐ MAD   ☐ BALLISTIC

4. Your dog throws up in your room.

☐ MIFFED   ☐ HACKED OFF

☐ MAD   ☐ BALLISTIC

5. You spill grape juice on your white T-shirt.

☐ MIFFED ☐ HACKED OFF

☐ MAD ☐ BALLISTIC

6. You slip and fall in a mud puddle on school picture day.

This stinks.

☐ MIFFED ☐ HACKED OFF

☐ MAD ☐ BALLISTIC

7. Your social studies teacher surprises you with a pop quiz.

☐ MIFFED ☐ HACKED OFF

☐ MAD ☐ BALLISTIC

A POP QUIZ!

8. You get floor burn while playing fleeceball in gym class.

☐ MIFFED

☐ HACKED OFF

☐ MAD

☐ BALLISTIC

9. Your archenemy beats you in chess.

☐ MIFFED

☐ HACKED OFF

☐ MAD

☐ BALLISTIC

ZAPPED!

Everyone knows that Ben Franklin flew kites. Did you know that Ben taught himself how to swim?

SUPER SCRIBBLE GAME

My scribble is a...

My caption:

FACT-TASTIC TRIVIA

Can you decode the answers to questions in Francis's *Fact-tastic Trivia* book? Use his code on page 58.

Q: What do you call the offspring of a male tiger and a female lion?

A: $\underline{}_{13} \ \underline{}_{6} \ \underline{}_{20} \ \underline{G}_{3} \ \underline{}_{23} \ \underline{}_{11} \ \underline{}_{21}$.

Q: What bird, extinct by 1681, was named for the Portuguese word for "stupid"?

A: $\underset{6}{\text{T}} \underset{1}{\text{H}} \underset{8}{\text{E}}$ $\underset{25}{} \underset{11}{} \underset{25}{} \underset{11}{}$ $\underset{7}{} \underset{20}{} \underset{14}{} \underset{25}{}$.

Q: What U.S. spider's poison is 15 times as powerful as a rattlesnake's venom?

A: $\underset{6}{} \underset{1}{} \underset{8}{}$ $\underset{7}{} \underset{23}{} \underset{13}{} \underset{26}{} \underset{12}{}$ $\underset{22}{} \underset{20}{} \underset{25}{} \underset{11}{} \underset{22}{}$.

FAMILY REUNION

Here's a snapshot from Nate's family reunion.

WHAT DOES YOURS LOOK LIKE?
DRAW IT!

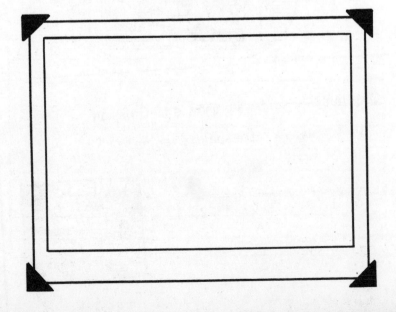

Q: What bird, extinct by 1681, was named for the Portuguese word for "stupid"?

A: $\overline{\underset{6}{T}}\ \overline{\underset{1}{H}}\ \overline{\underset{8}{E}}$

$\overline{\underset{25}{}}\ \overline{\underset{11}{}}\ \overline{\underset{25}{}}\ \overline{\underset{11}{}}\ \ \overline{\underset{7}{}}\ \overline{\underset{20}{}}\ \overline{\underset{14}{}}\ \overline{\underset{25}{}}$.

Q: What U.S. spider's poison is 15 times as powerful as a rattlesnake's venom?

A: $\overline{\underset{6}{}}\ \overline{\underset{1}{}}\ \overline{\underset{8}{}}\ \ \overline{\underset{7}{}}\ \overline{\underset{23}{}}\ \overline{\underset{13}{}}\ \overline{\underset{26}{}}\ \overline{\underset{12}{}}$

$\overline{\underset{22}{}}\ \overline{\underset{20}{}}\ \overline{\underset{25}{}}\ \overline{\underset{11}{}}\ \overline{\underset{22}{}}$.

FAMILY REUNION

Here's a snapshot from Nate's family reunion.

WHAT DOES YOURS LOOK LIKE?
DRAW IT!

WRITE DOWN THE FAVOURITE
PART OF YOUR FAMILY REUNION.

WRITE DOWN THE MOST ANNOYING
PART OF YOUR FAMILY REUNION.

ADVENTURES WITH ARTUR

Poor Nate! He's up against his archrival, Artur, again, and this doesn't look good! Fill in the speech bubbles and finish this comic.

PSYCHO DOGS RULE

Nate's superstar fleece-ball team (the Kuddle Kittens, according to Gina) has a lineup of nine kids. Can you hit a home run and arrange each initial so that it only shows up once in each row, column, and box?

(N) = NATE

(P) = PAIGE

(T) = TEDDY

(S) = SARAH

(F) = FRANCIS

(M) = MARCIE

(G) = GINA

(C) = CHAD

(W) = WILL

dribble dribble dribble

N		T		F	G	W		
	W		P					G
G		S					F	M
	M		N				W	
P				W	F	S		
T				G				N
C		M			P	T	F	
	S		G			M	P	
					S			C

THE HERO

Who will come to Jenny's rescue?

PAGE O'DOODLES

Bust that boredom! It's doodle time –
see how fast you can fill the page.

KING OF JOBS

THERE MUST BE **SOMETHING** I CAN DO, OR SELL, OR...

Someday Nate would love to be a professional cartoonist. What if you could have a job that nobody else had? Combine the words below and create the most exciting jobs you can think of.

SENIOR

DESIGNER

LUXURY

EXPERT

DREAM

TRUCK

PONY

TEACHER

RACER

CROSS COUNTRY

HOT-AIR BALLOON

SAILBOAT

HAT

CIRCUS

DRIVER

MARSHMALLOW

ENGINEER

SALESPERSON

SINGING

SPORTSCAR

OCEAN

RACING HORSE

TASTER

PAINTER

CREATOR

TAP DANCER

TESTER

BUILDER

DIVER

HAMMOCK

RESORT

ICE CREAM

SCULPTOR

FINDING A NEW WAY TO EARN MONEY!

Here are some one-of-a-kind jobs!

SENIOR HAMMOCK TESTER

SINGING HOT-AIR BALLOON SALESPERSON

NOW WRITE DOWN YOURS!

_____

_____

_____

_____

_____

_____

_____

_____

_____

_____

_____

_____

_____

IT'S YOUR CALL!

What will happen when brainiac Francis goes up against Randy the bully? Will Mrs Hickson save the day? You decide! Create a comic that tells the story.

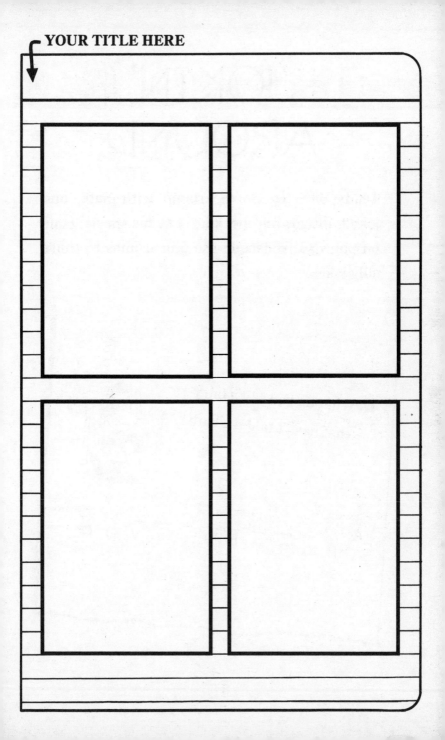

YOUR TITLE HERE

JOKIN' AROUND

Teddy likes to clown around with Nate, and joke telling is his specialty! Use his special code on page 34 to decode the punch lines to these silly jokes.

Q: What do you call a fairy that hasn't taken a bath?

A: $\underline{}_{H}\ \underline{}_{G}\ \underline{}_{R}\ \underline{}_{M}\ \underline{}_{P}\ \underline{}_{V}\ \underline{}_{I}\ \underline{}_{Y}\ \underline{}_{V}\ \underline{}_{O}\ \underline{}_{O}$

Q: What did the chewing gum say to the shoe?

A: __'__ __ __ __ __ __ __ __ __.
   R N   H G F X P   L M

  __ __ __.
  B L F

SNICKER!
HEH HEH
HA!

Q: What is the difference between here and there?

A: __ __ __ __ __ __ __ __ __ "__."
   G S V   O V G G V I   G

U R CAR2NING!

Create your own comic using Gina's toy, Kuddles, plus Nate and Coach!

YOUR TITLE HERE

DESTINED FOR GREATNESS

How will Nate surpass all others? He has so many talents. Fill out the grid so that the first letter of each skill shows up only once in every row, column, and box.

 S = **SOCCER**

M = **MUSIC**

 C = **CARTOONING**

T = **TABLE FOOTBALL**

THE DOCTOR IS IN!

Uh-oh! What is Doctor Cesspool up to?
Fill in the speech bubbles and decide what's happening!

SCRIBBLE, SCRIBBLE

Turn this scribble into a _____ picture.
(beautiful, scary, weird, funny...)

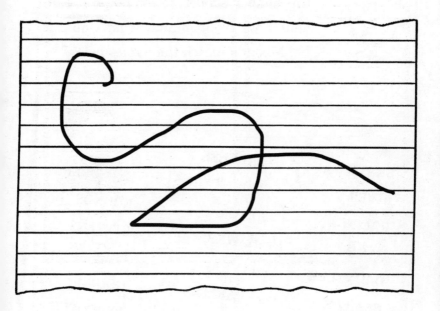

Give your art a caption!

SUPER TROOPER

Nate is really proud to be a member of the Timber Scouts. If you could create your own troop name, what would it be? Mix and match the names below!

BRAVE	BADGERS	RAVENS
RIVER	MOUNTAIN	EXPLORERS
RACING	BEARS	HOUNDS
DARING	HAWKS	KITTENS
DAUNTLESS	FLYING	EAGLES
CAMELS	FEARLESS	GUIDES
SUN	WARRIOR	PEACOCKS
COURAGEOUS	HAPPY	CATS
RUNNING	MOON	BULLS
PLATYPUSES	PURPLE	LUCKY

LIST YOUR TOP TROOP NAMES HERE!

_____

_____

_____

_____

_____

_____

_____

_____

_____

_____

_____

_____

_____

THE GRAND PRIZE

Help Nate land the first prize!

DOODLE DRAMA

Do you fill your notebooks with cartoons and doodles, just like Nate? Go ahead – fill the page!

U DRAW IT!

Anything could happen! Create a comic using all three characters below.

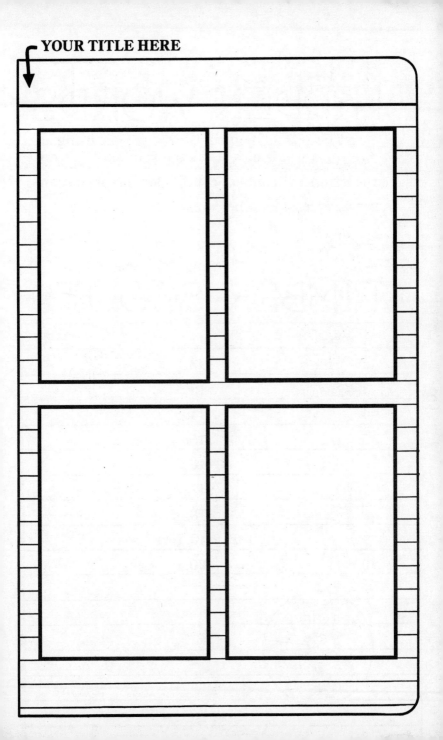

YOUR TITLE HERE

HIDDEN WORDS

Are you a wordsmith? Let's see your skills! Using the letters in "Timber Scout" below, see if you can create at least 20 other words!

TIMBER SCOUT

1. met	11.
2.	12.
3.	13.
4.	14.
5.	15.
6.	16.
7.	17.
8.	18.
9.	19. tore
10.	20.

LET'S
SEE HERE

BELIEVE IT OR NOT?

Francis is like a walking encyclopedia. Use his code on page 58 to find out what he knows.

$\overline{19}\ \overline{8}\ \overline{21}\ \overline{10}\ \overline{24}\ \ \overline{20}\ \overline{24}\ \ \ \overline{6}\ \overline{1}\ \overline{8}$

$\overline{11}\ \overline{21}\ \overline{23}\ \overline{9}\ \ \overline{2}\ \overline{23}\ \overline{13}\ \overline{21}\ \overline{8}\ \overline{6}$

$\overline{6}\ \overline{1}\ \overline{13}\ \overline{6}\ \ \overline{14}\ \overline{11}\ \overline{6}\ \overline{13}\ \overline{6}\ \overline{8}\ \overline{24}$

$\overline{26}\ \overline{23}\ \overline{11}\ \overline{26}\ \overline{12}\ \overline{22}\ \overline{20}\ \overline{24}\ \overline{8}\ .$

$\overline{13}\ \ \overline{25}\ \overline{10}\ \overline{26}\ \overline{12}\ \overline{24}$,

$\overline{15}\ \overline{10}\ \overline{13}\ \overline{26}\ \overline{12}\ \ \overline{25}\ \overline{11}\ \overline{8}\ \overline{24}$

$\overline{21}\ \overline{11}\ \overline{6}\ \ \overline{8}\ \overline{26}\ \overline{1}\ \overline{11}\ .$

$\overline{18}\ \overline{11}\ \overline{24}\ \overline{6}\quad\overline{25}\ \overline{10}\ \overline{24}\ \overline{6}$

$\overline{2}\ \overline{13}\ \overline{14}\ \overline{6}\ \overline{20}\ \overline{26}\ \overline{23}\ \overline{8}\ \overline{24}\quad\overline{20}\ \overline{21}$

$\overline{9}\ \overline{11}\ \overline{10}\ \overline{14}\quad\overline{1}\ \overline{11}\ \overline{10}\ \overline{24}\ \overline{8}\quad\overline{13}\ \overline{14}\ \overline{8}$

 $\overline{18}\ \overline{13}\ \overline{25}\ \overline{8}\quad\overline{16}\ \overline{14}\ \overline{11}\ \overline{18}$

$\overline{25}\ \overline{8}\ \overline{13}\ \overline{25}\quad\overline{24}\ \overline{12}\ \overline{20}\ \overline{21}$.

$\overline{6}\ \overline{1}\ \overline{8}\quad\overline{8}\ \overline{23}\ \overline{8}\ \overline{2}\ \overline{1}\ \overline{13}\ \overline{21}\ \overline{6}\quad\overline{20}\ \overline{24}$

$\overline{6}\ \overline{1}\ \overline{8}\quad\overline{11}\ \overline{21}\ \overline{23}\ \overline{9}$

$\overline{18}\ \overline{13}\ \overline{18}\ \overline{18}\ \overline{13}\ \overline{23}$

,

$\overline{6}\ \overline{1}\ \overline{13}\ \overline{6}\quad\overline{26}\ \overline{13}\ \overline{21}\ \overline{6}\quad\overline{4}\ \overline{10}\ \overline{18}\ \overline{2}$.

GREAT NATE FACTS

How well do YOU know Nate Wright? Take this quiz and find out!

1. Nate once spilled egg salad on this person's head.

a. Randy

b. Jenny

c. Gina

d. Dad

2. Nate lost this, his most prized possession, in a creek!

a. Comic book

b. Soccer ball

c. Skateboard

d. Timber Scout beret

3. This is not one of Nate's after-school jobs.

    a. Arranging garden gnomes

    b. Pulling weeds for Mr Galvin

    c. Walking Spitsy

    d. Selling comic books to Gordie

4. This is the name of one of Nate's comic book characters.

    a. Maureen Biology

    b. Dr Danger Stranger

    c. Professor Feardawn

    d. Randy Rottenwood

5. Nate chopped off a garden gnome's head with whose sword?

    a. Teddy

    b. Gina

    c. Kevin

    d. Chad

DESIGN TIME

Using your super scout names from page 131,
design a troop symbol for each one!

HERE'S NATE'S TIMBER SCOUT SYMBOL:

NOW DRAW YOURS!

_____ _____ _____
_____ _____ _____

**WRITE THE MATCHING
SCOUT NAME BELOW EACH INSIGNIA.**

Check out Nate's cool scout uniform –
the beret, the necktie, and the arm patch
with his scout symbol!

BERET

CLIP-ON
NECKERCHIEF

NAME
STITCHED
ON SHIRT

TIMBER
SCOUT
INSIGNIA

MERIT
BADGES

SPORTY
STRIPE

DESIGN YOUR OWN AWESOME UNIFORM:

RATS!

Do you ever have moments that turn into total disasters? Nate does! Where Nate goes, trouble follows.

LIST YOUR WORST DISASTER MOMENTS HERE!

1.

2.

3.

4.

5.

6.

7. You get picked dead last for kickball in gym class.

8.

9.

10.

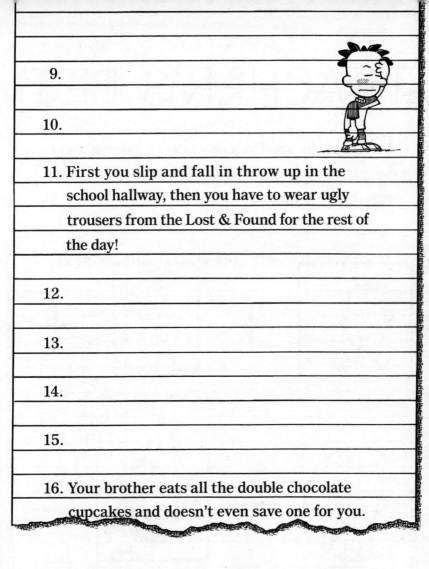

11. First you slip and fall in throw up in the school hallway, then you have to wear ugly trousers from the Lost & Found for the rest of the day!

12.

13.

14.

15.

16. Your brother eats all the double chocolate cupcakes and doesn't even save one for you.

TEACHER'S PET

What happens when you put 3 Goody Two-Shoes in a room with Mrs Godfrey? You decide! Create a comic with these characters:

Goody Two-Shoe #1   Goody Two-Shoe #2

Goody Two-Shoe #3

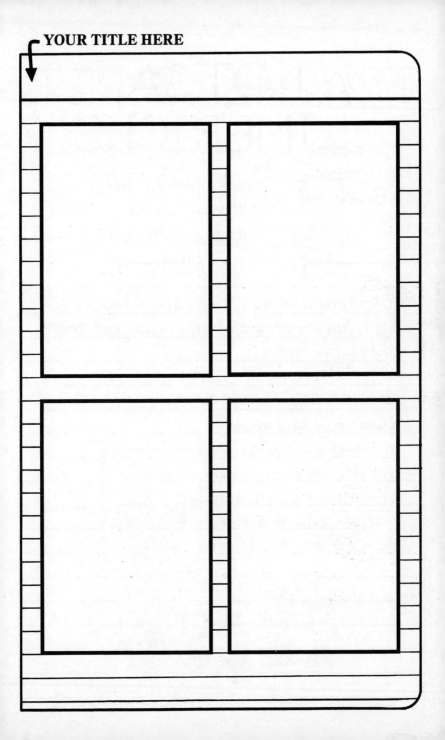

YOUR TITLE HERE

LOTSA LIMERICKS

Nate's a master of rhyme.
With verse he is fine.
But he's given the sign –
It's your turn this time!

Try writing a limerick. That's a poem with 5 lines,
where the 1ˢᵗ, 2ⁿᵈ, and 5ᵗʰ lines rhyme, and the 3ʳᵈ
and 4ᵗʰ lines rhyme.

HERE'S NATE'S EXAMPLE:

LIMERICK by Nate Wright

I have feasted on all sorts of noodles,

I have tried an assortment of strudels.

Of the foods that I've eaten,

Only one can't be beaten:

An extra-large bag of Cheez Doodles.

NOW, YOU TRY!

There once was a kid from <u>Peru</u>,

Who came down with a terrible _____.

He gave out a <u>cry</u>,

And yelled out "Oh,_____ ,"

Then left on a train right at <u>two</u>.

NOT TOO **SHABBY!**

A little girl wanted a <u>llama</u>,

She decided to go ask her _____ ,

It ran and it <u>ate</u>,

And never was _____ ,

But still it caused all kinds of <u>drama</u>.

The class clown of P.S. <u>38</u>,

He goes by the name of Big _____ .

He loves to eat <u>oodles</u>

Of orange Cheez _____

And thinks that he's awesome and _____ !

Doodle
oodle
noodle
strudel
poodle
caboodle

ON OFF

WRITE YOUR OWN LIMERICKS!

There once was a fellow named Chad,

_____,

_____,

_____,

_____.

Oh, how I love pizza with cheese,

_____,

_____,

_____,

_____.

...BUT LET'S AVOID ANY MORE POEMS ABOUT JUNK FOOD, SHALL WE?

SPORTS SCENE

Teddy is a huge fan of sports trivia. Use his special code on page 34 to decode the answers to this super sports quiz!

Q: What gem do baseball players play on?

A: $\underline{\quad}$ $\underline{\quad}$ $\underline{\quad}$ $\underline{\quad}$ $\underline{\quad}$ $\underline{\quad}$ $\underline{\quad}$ $\underline{\quad}$.
Z W R Z N L M W

Q: What are the most home runs hit by one player in a single major league game?

A: $\underline{\quad}$ $\underline{\quad}$ $\underline{\quad}$ $\underline{\quad}$.
U L F I

Q: How many events are in the heptathlon?

A: $\underline{\quad}$ $\underline{\quad}$ $\underline{\quad}$ $\underline{\quad}$ $\underline{\quad}$.
H V E V M

SAY IT LOUD!

What's going on in each picture? It's up to you! Fill in the speech bubbles and finish each story.

⊕◓⊕ ◓⊕⊕⊕ ◒⊕⊕◒⊕
⊕⊕⊕◒ ⊕◒⊕⊕⊕◒?

◒⊕⊕◒⊕ ⊕⊕⊕◒ ⊕◒⊕⊕⊕◒⊕⊕!

SCHOOL PICTURE DAY

Nate draws comics based on his own true-life moments! The best AND the worst!

NOW YOU TRY!
WRITE DOWN YOUR FAVOURITE PART
OF SCHOOL PICTURE DAY.

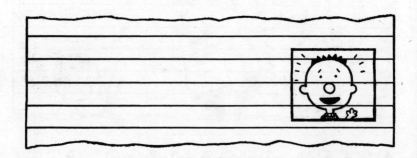

WRITE DOWN THE MOST ANNOYING PART OF SCHOOL PICTURE DAY.

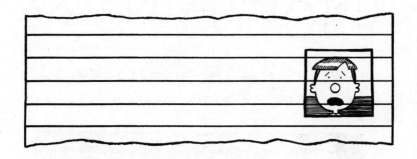

DRAW YOURSELF ON SCHOOL PICTURE DAY!

CAPTION CAPTAIN

I FOUND YOUR "WARM FUZZIES" BROCHURE ON THE KITCHEN FLOOR.

For his scout troop, Nate has to sell cheesy wall hangings called Warm Fuzzies. Check out these off-the-wall captions!

YOU'RE MY SWEETIE PIE!

I'M A NUT!

HANG IN THERE!

NOW CREATE YOUR OWN CAPTIONS FOR THE FOLLOWING FUNNY POSTERS!

_____

_____

_____

_____

_____

_____

_____

_____

_____

_____

WHO'S A BRAINIAC?

Francis is one smart scout! And he loves learning strange factoids. Use his code on page 58 to uncover this weird and funny trivia.

$\overline{24}\ \overline{11}\ \overline{18}\ \overline{8}$

$\overline{6}\ \overline{10}\ \overline{14}\ \overline{6}\ \overline{23}\ \overline{8}\ \overline{24}$

$\overline{26}\ \overline{13}\ \overline{21}$

$\overline{7}\ \overline{14}\ \overline{8}\ \overline{13}\ \overline{6}\ \overline{1}\ \overline{8}$

$\overline{6}\ \overline{1}\ \overline{14}\ \overline{11}\ \overline{10}\ \overline{3}\ \overline{1}$

$\overline{6}\ \overline{1}\ \overline{8}\ \overline{20}\ \overline{14}\ \ \overline{7}\ \overline{10}\ \overline{6}\ \overline{6}\ \overline{24}$.

$\overline{}\ \overline{}\ \overline{}\ \overline{}\ \overline{23}\ \overline{24}$
2 8 13 14 23 24

$\overline{18}\ \overline{8}\ \overline{23}\ \overline{6}$
18 8 23 6

$\overline{20}\ \overline{21}\quad \overline{19}\ \overline{20}\ \overline{21}\ \overline{8}\ \overline{3}\ \overline{13}\ \overline{14}$.

NATE!

HOLD UP!

$\overline{13}\quad \overline{7}\ \overline{10}\ \overline{6}\ \overline{6}\ \overline{8}\ \overline{14}\ \overline{16}\ \overline{23}\ \overline{9}$

$\overline{1}\ \overline{13}\ \overline{24}\quad \overline{6}\ \overline{22}\ \overline{8}\ \overline{23}\ \overline{19}\ \overline{8}$

$\overline{6}\ \overline{1}\ \overline{11}\ \overline{10}\ \overline{24}\ \overline{13}\ \overline{21}\ \overline{25}$

$\overline{8}\ \overline{9}\ \overline{8}\ \overline{24}$.

LAUGH-A-THON

Nate's maths teacher, Mr Staples, always tells lame jokes. What makes you laugh out loud? It's time to joke around! Fill in the punch lines!

Q: What kind of dog tells time?

A: A _____ dog!

Q: What do cats eat for breakfast?

A: _____ Crispies!

Q: How do you communicate with a fish?

A: Drop him a _____ !

WHAT COULD GO WRONG?

How will Nate's walk to the park with Spitsy turn out?

EXCLAMATION STATION

What's going on in each picture? You decide!
Fill in the speech bubbles below.

_____

_____

⊕⬤⊕ ⊕⬤⬤⊕⊕ ⬤⊕⬤⊕!

⊕⬤⊕, ⊕⊕ ⊕⊕ ⊕⬤⬤!

FUNNY
BUSINESS

Teddy's one funny guy! Use his secret code on page 34 to uncover the punch lines to his favourite jokes below.

Q: Why was the belt arrested?

A: $\overline{}\,\overline{}\,\overline{}$ $\overline{}\,\overline{}\,\overline{}\,\overline{}\,\overline{}\,\overline{}\,\overline{}$
   U L I   S L O W R M T

$\overline{}\,\overline{}$ $\overline{}\,\overline{}\,\overline{}$ $\overline{}\,\overline{}\,\overline{}\,\overline{}\,\overline{}$.
   F K   G S V   K Z M G H

Q: Why are teddy bears never hungry?

A: _ _ _ _ _ _ _
Y V X Z F H V

_ _ _ _   _ _ _
G S V B   Z I V

_ _ _ _ _ _
Z O D Z B H

_ _ _ _ _ _ _ .
H G F U U V W

Q: Why didn't the hot dog star in the movie?

A: _ _ _   _ _ _ _ _
G S V   I L O V H

_ _ _ _ _ _ ,
D V I V M G

_ _ _ _
T L L W

_ _ _ _ _ _ .
V M L F T S

SCRIBBLE MASTER

Who's the scribble master? You are!
Make a work of art out of this scribble!

Remember the caption!

NATE'S NAME GAME

Nate invented a name game. For each letter in a person's first name, write down an adjective (see page 7 for the definition) or phrase that describes him or her, beginning with that letter!

HERE'S WHAT
NATE WROTE
FOR ARTUR,
HIS RIVAL.

➥

ANNOYING

REASONABLY NICE

TALENTED

UNFORTUNATELY,

REALLY IRRITATING

NOW YOU TRY!

N _____

A WESOME

T _____

E _____

E_____

LOVES UNICORNS

L_____

E_____

N_____

I'LL TAKE THIS ONE.

ADOPT A UNICORN!

GRADE OBSESSED

I_____

N_____

A_____

A+   HONOUR ROLL

FACT FINDER

R_____

A_____

N_____

C_____

I_____

S_____

For MY book, I chose a FASCINATING volume of TRIVIA!

T ELLS JOKES

E _____

D _____

D _____

Y _____

J _____

E _____

N ATE'S DREAM GIRL

N _____

Y _____

NOW TRY YOUR NAME!

_____

_____

_____

_____

_____

_____

_____

YOUR PORTRAIT

LOCKER DISASTER

Watch out! Nate's locker is overflowing... AGAIN.
Solve the clues to the puzzle and find every item inside!

ACROSS

3. Nate wears this to scout meetings – the beret is the best part!

5. It's filled with numbers, and Nate needs to read it for Mr Staples's class. Rhymes with "bath hook."

7. After school, Nate sometimes kicks this around with his friends.

9. Mmm, orange and puffalicious, these are Nate's favourite snack.

10. Nate loves to draw these, especially where he's Ultra-Nate, the superhero.

11. This little piece of pink paper means that Nate has to stay after class!

12. Nate cruises the neighbourhood on these cool wheels. Riding this is like surfing, only better!

DOWN

1. Nate gets them at Pu Pu Panda, and thinks they taste like Styrofoam.

2. Nate's feet are smelly, so these can get gross after gym class.

4. Nate didn't get a very good grade in Mrs Godfrey's class on his _____ .

6. Nate wrote this rhyming masterpiece to Jenny, his crush, in Ms Clarke's class.

8. Nate would rather be cartooning than doing this. Not schoolwork, but _____ .

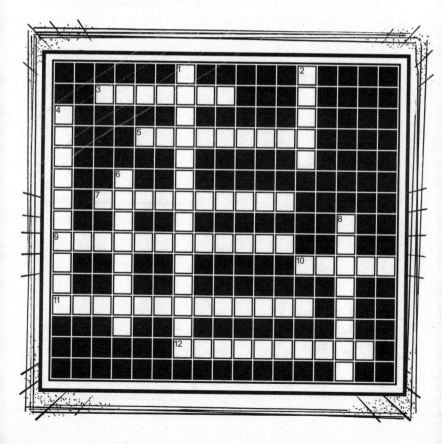

COPY CAT

Are you an awesome artist? Test your skills. Try drawing each of these characters in the blank boxes below.

WHAT WAS THE QUESTION AGAIN?

Francis is one smart student. He even listens to Mr Galvin! Use his code on page 58 to find the answers to these cool questions about the Earth.

What is the name of the largest ocean on Earth?

$\overline{}$ $\overline{}$ $\overline{}$ $\overline{}$ $\overline{}$ $\overline{}$ $\overline{}$
2 13 26 20 16 20 26

$\overline{}$ $\overline{}$ $\overline{}$ $\overline{}$ $\overline{}$.
11 26 8 13 21

The mass of the Earth is made up mostly of which two elements?

$$\overline{}_{20}\ \overline{}_{14}\ \overline{}_{11}\ \overline{}_{21}$$

$$\overline{}_{13}\ \overline{}_{21}\ \overline{}_{25}$$

$$\overline{}_{11}\ \overline{}_{17}\ \overline{}_{9}\ \overline{}_{3}\ \overline{}_{8}\ \overline{}_{21}.$$

Outside of Antarctica, what is the largest desert in the world?

$$\overline{}_{6}\ \overline{}_{1}\ \overline{}_{8}$$

$$\overline{}_{24}\ \overline{}_{13}\ \overline{}_{1}\ \overline{}_{13}\ \overline{}_{14}\ \overline{}_{13}.$$

HAPPINESS IS...
WARM FUZZIES

Sell the most wall hangings for the Timber Scouts and win a GREAT prize. Fill in the blanks so that each wall hanging is represented only once in every row, column, and box!

N = I'M A NUT

W = WHO, ME?

S = SEAL OF APPROVAL

F = FOLLOW YOUR RAINBOW

U = ADOPT A UNICORN

H = I NEED A HUG!

G = DON'T YOU LOVE ... GRANDMAS?

L = LOVE IS ... SHARING

S	U	W		L		F	
		F					N
			H		G		
H	G	L		N			W
W	S	H		L			F
	L	W			U		
							S
G	L	N		F			

BUBBLE TROUBLE

Nate's in trouble, again. Fill in the speech bubbles
and find out what's happening!

CARTOON CRAZE

Nate's a master at cartooning. He even has his own comics collection with characters he's created, like Doctor Cesspool. Create your own comics villains and heroes by mixing and matching the following names!

DARING	SILVER	PROFESSOR
MAGNIFICENT	DETECTIVE	_____
INVISIBLE	BLOB	CLIMBER
_____	MASTERMIND	_____
OUTRAGEOUS	PRINCE	DISASTER
MYSTERIOUS	HEIRESS	LICORICE
MAD	_____	MIDNIGHT
SLIMY	MAGICIAN	PILOT
MAGNETIC	CLOWN	GOLD TOOTH
ULTIMATE	DISAPPEARING	PINK

HERE ARE SOME
WILD CHARACTER NAMES:

Slimy Prince Disaster

Professor Licorice Midnight

NOW MAKE UP YOUR OWN!

_____ _____ _____

_____ _____ _____

_____ _____ _____

_____ _____ _____

_____ _____ _____

_____ _____ _____

_____ _____ _____

_____ _____ _____

_____ _____ _____

_____ _____ _____

_____ _____ _____

Maureen Biology!

Dr Arch Enemy!

ALL MIXED UP!

What do all of these words have in common? Each one adds to the action in *Big Nate on a Roll*, book 3, where Nate runs into all kinds of trouble!

ARTUR

MALL COP

JAMBOREE

GORDIE

BUMBLE BOY

TOY POODLE

SCENERY

BROWNIES

MR EUSTIS

SKATEBOARD

WARM FUZZIES

GNOMES

SPITSY

COMIC BOOK

PRIZES

FUNDRAISER

ROCKIN' ROBOT

TELESCOPE

TIMBER SCOUTS

Find more than 15 of the words in the puzzle below and help Nate in his mission to beat Artur, aka Mr Perfect!

T	O	B	O	R	N	I	K	C	O	R	Y	E	S	C
P	I	Y	R	S	E	M	O	N	G	Y	S	I	C	C
R	O	M	B	O	K	P	O	T	R	M	T	D	E	G
I	S	C	B	P	W	A	E	U	S	S	I	R	N	I
Z	E	R	L	E	T	N	T	E	U	T	P	O	E	L
E	O	E	C	L	R	R	I	E	R	B	S	G	R	A
S	E	S	C	A	A	S	R	E	B	O	S	Y	Y	E
O	L	I	E	O	E	M	C	S	S	O	B	L	O	M
B	D	A	I	P	M	Y	L	O	H	T	A	M	B	E
R	O	R	I	S	E	I	Z	Z	U	F	M	R	A	W
C	O	D	Z	A	E	O	C	M	R	T	Y	M	D	J
S	P	N	C	L	L	C	O	B	O	O	S	E	O	I
T	Y	U	T	E	L	E	S	C	O	P	E	A	E	O
S	O	F	B	U	M	B	L	E	B	O	Y	E	I	A
S	T	E	E	E	T	B	C	J	O	O	K	I	O	C

HE'S *PERFECT!*

LOOOVE IT!

What do you love most?
Rate these from 1 to 10.
10 = BIG LOVE
1 = JUST OK

	RATING
Hot fudge sundae	_____
A water slide	_____
When your teacher gives you an A	_____
Going camping with your family	_____
Breakfast for dinner	_____
Playing at the beach	_____
Slumber party with your best friends	_____
Making a super-cool video or drawing	_____

Getting a puppy   —

Watching fireworks   —

Finding out your crush likes you back   —

Dancing like crazy   —

Summer vacation   —

Opening birthday presents   —

Climbing a tree   —

Performing in a killer band   —

Becoming captain of the team   —

Eating the last cookie   —

NATE'S COMIX CRACK-UP

Nate's comic book is a masterpiece. Solve the maze and figure out who's dying to buy a copy!

TAKE A HIKE

Nate and his scout troop are on the move.
Fill in the speech bubbles and finish the story!

SUPER WRITER

Nate's a superstar at making up silly rhymes. Now you try! Answer each of these clues with a two-word phrase that rhymes!

EXAMPLE:

Overweight feline <u>F</u> <u>A</u> <u>T</u> <u>C</u> <u>A</u> <u>T</u>

1. Friendly rodents <u>N</u> _ _ _ _ _ <u>C</u> _

2. Feathered animal,
   a group of them <u>B</u> _ _ _ _ _ _ _ _ <u>D</u>

3. Beach-covered
   sweets _ _ _ <u>D</u> _ <u>C</u> _ _ _ _ _

4. A long distance away,
   it twinkles in the night sky _ _ <u>R</u> _ <u>T</u> _ _ _

5. You just bought it,
   and you wear it on your foot <u>N</u> _ _ _ <u>H</u> _ _

6. What your dog drinks from _ _ **P** _ **C** _ _

7. Colour that rhymes with "head"

   The place where you sleep _ **E** _ _ _ _ **D**

8. A partner who isn't on time

   _ _ _ **T** _ **M** _ _ _ _

IT'S YOUR TURN!
MAKE UP TWO-WORD PHRASES THAT RHYME
AND WRITE CLUES THAT DESCRIBE THEM.

9.

10.

THINK THINK THINK THINK THINK THINK THINK THINK THINK THINK THINK

WHO'S A SPORTS GENIUS?

Are you a sports whiz like Teddy?

Use his code on page 34 to decipher the answers.

Q: Which three events make up the triathlon?

A: _ _ _ _ _ _ _ _ _ ,
H D R N N R M T

_ _ _ _ _ _ _ , _ _ _
X B X O R M T   Z M W

_ _ _ _ _ _ _ .
I F M M R M T

RACE YOU GUYS TO THE FLAGPOLE!

! !

Q: What sport features strikers and sweepers?

A: _ _ _ _ _ _ .
H L X X V I

Q: What racket sport involves hitting a bird?

A: _ _ _ _ _ _ _ _ _ .
Y Z W N R M G L M

Q: What are the steps in the triple jump?

A: _ _ _ , _ _ _ _ ,
S L K   H P R K

_ _ _ _ _ _ .
Z M W Q F N K

COMIX-O-RAMA!

It looks like detention is calling… What happens when Nate runs up against his dad AND a substitute teacher in one day? It's up to you!

YOUR TITLE HERE

CATS AND DOGS

Spitsy has a serious crush on Francis's cat, Pickles. But how much do cats and dogs really have in common? Solve the clues to the puzzle and find out!

ACROSS

2. A cat will almost never meow at another _____ . This sound is reserved for humans.

3. Dalmatian puppies are pure _____ at birth.

5. A dog's nose works about one _____ times more efficiently than the human nose.

7. Most pet owners say their pet makes them really happy. They _____ more than once a day.

8. Superman's _____ was named Krypto.

10. Charlie Brown's dog is named _____ .

11. Cats usually have 12 _____ on each side of their noses.

13. An adult cat has 30 teeth in its _____ .

16. Cats are carnivores, which means they eat _____ .

17. Dogs sweat from the pads on their _____ (rhymes with "laws"). They discharge heat by panting.

18. A cat in a hurry can sprint at about thirty-one miles per _____ .

DOWN

1. Calico cats are almost always this gender.

2. Among the seven _____ , only icy Antarctica remains catless today.

4. The first seeing-eye dog was presented to a _____ person on April 25, 1938 (rhymes with "mind").

6. Cats can _____ 5 times their height (rhymes with "bump").

8. It takes 63 _____ for puppies to be born (rhymes with "ways").

9. The chow chow has a black _____ . Other dogs have pink ones.

12. Cats have existed longer than _____ .

14. There are 42 _____ in a dog's mouth.

15. Cats _____ on their toes.

FREAKY FACTS

Francis loves learning wild facts like these. Test your brain with these trivia questions, then uncover the answers using his secret code on page 58.

Q: What is the biggest planet in our solar system?

A: $\overline{}_{4}\ \overline{}_{10}\ \overline{}_{2}\ \overline{}_{20}\ \overline{}_{6}\ \overline{}_{8}\ \overline{}_{14}$.

Q: What's the highest mountain on Earth?

A: $\overline{}_{18} \ \overline{}_{11} \ \overline{}_{10} \ \overline{}_{21} \ \overline{}_{6}$

$\overline{}_{8} \ \overline{}_{19} \ \overline{}_{8} \ \overline{}_{14} \ \overline{}_{8} \ \overline{}_{24} \ \overline{}_{6}$.

Q: What is the name of the closest star to Earth?

A: $\overline{}_{6} \ \overline{}_{1} \ \overline{}_{8} \ \ \overline{}_{24} \ \overline{}_{10} \ \overline{}_{21}$.

JUICY GOSSIP

Nate writes a gossip column about his teachers, and it's a gas! Fill in the squares so that each teacher's initial appears only once in every row, column, and box.

C = **MS CLARKE**

R = **MR ROSA**

G = **MR GALVIN**

J = **COACH JOHN**

NOTORIOUS
NATE TRIVIA

1. Nate once called Chad by the wrong name. What was it?

a. Bob

b. Randy

c. Todd

d. Gordie

2. Nate's Little League team was once sponsored by which business?

a. Franny's Pizza

b. Patsy's Pancake House

c. Nate's Noodles

d. Joe's Hot Dogs

... "WE'RE ON A ROLL"!!

3. What was the name of the mascot for Nate's fleeceball team?

a. Puffy

b. Kuddles

c. Killer Bee

d. McWinky

4. Which of Nate's rivals gets a bloody nose?

a. Chester

b. Gina

c. Artur

d. Randy

5. What does Gina sometimes call Nate?

a. El Stupido

b. Spiky-Haired Kid

c. Pinhead

d. Ultra-Nate

LOST IN THE WOODS

Help! Nate and his scout troop have gone down the wrong trail. Find all the camping words in the puzzle, and get Nate and his friends back to civilization!

MAP

FLASHLIGHT

TENT

TRAIL MIX

COMPASS

BACKPACK

SLEEPING BAG

HIKING BOOTS

CAMPFIRE

SUNSCREEN

INSECT REPELLENT

WATCH

OUTDOORS

BUGS

RAIN GEAR

BINOCULARS

WATER BOTTLE

MOUNTAIN

FIRST AID KIT

CANOE

```
N R M R H E B F T D A U W E T
D F G T P A U O N E H W G X A
O T R A I L M I X G N A S A T
S T O O B G N I K I H T R S I
I S G U B G I W M T H E E U K
T R C N T E N O E G O R C N D
A A N A O D U I I H R B O S I
N L B N M N O L P A U O M C A
O U A A T P H O I E A T P R T
H C P A C S F N R N E T A E S
C O I N A K G I B S P L S E R
T N E L L E P E R T C E S N I
A I F L A A K A A E O F A C F
W B K R K T S O C U E M G B U
S A N N F P A R S K N C I R U
```

GOSH, this is a steep mountain!

We're not even ON the mountain yet!

COMIX CAPER

Draw a comic strip featuring the following
characters. Anything goes!

YOUR TITLE HERE

PRACTICAL JOKESTER

Teddy is a huge fan of corny jokes! Use his code on page 34 to find out the punch lines.

Q: What did the beach say when the tide came in?

A: $\overline{}\ \overline{}\ \overline{}\ \overline{}\ \ \overline{}\ \overline{}\ \overline{}\ \overline{}$
O L M T G R N V

$\overline{}\ \overline{}\ \ \overline{}\ \overline{}\ \overline{}$.
M L H V Z

HEH
HEH!

Q: What did one potato chip say to the other?

A: $\overline{}\ \overline{}\ \overline{}\ \overline{}\ \overline{}\ \ \overline{}\ \overline{}$
H S Z O O D V

$\overline{}\ \overline{}\ \ \overline{}\ \overline{}\ \overline{}\ \ \overline{}$
T L U L I Z

$\overline{}\ \overline{}\ \overline{}$?
W R K

HA   HA

HEE

OPERATION CREATION

What went wrong with Doctor Cesspool's operation?

LUCKY DAY

Do you lead a charmed life?
Write down your luckiest moments ever,
then rate them from 1 to 10, 10 being the best!

LUCKY MOMENT	YES!	RATING
1.		___
2.		___
3.		___
4.		___
5.		___
6.		___
7. Your dad packs Cheez Doodles in your lunch.		___
8.		___
9.		___

10. ———

11. ———

12. You find a 10-dollar
bill on the way
to school. ———

13. ———

14. ———

15. ———

16. ———

17. ———

18. School's closed for a snow day. ———

ANSWER KEY

HOW WELL DO U KNOW NATE? (pp. 1–3)
1. (d) Throwing a pie in his face
2. (c) Teddy pretended his science lab squid was a booger.
3. (b) Scorpio
4. (d) Ultra-Nate
5. (e) Psycho Dogs

CODE CRACKER (pp. 4–5)
Gina loves Francis. FALSE
Nate gets a black eye riding his skateboard. FALSE
Teddy's dad is troop leader. TRUE
Nate eats rice cakes. FALSE
Spitsy has a crush on Ketchup the cat. FALSE

SCOUT'S HONOUR (pp. 12–13)

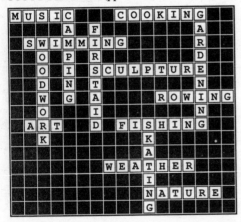

MOST VALUABLE PLAYER (p. 14)

SEMAPHORE SUPERSTAR (p. 15)
Remember this page. You'll need it later!

UN-YUMMY TREATS (pp. 16–17)

K	O	S	P	J	W	C	I	L
J	I	C	K	S	L	O	W	P
L	P	W	C	I	O	J	K	S
I	J	P	W	C	S	K	L	O
C	L	K	I	O	P	S	J	W
S	W	O	L	K	J	P	C	I
W	K	J	O	P	I	L	S	C
O	C	L	S	W	K	I	P	J
P	S	I	J	L	C	W	O	K

IT'S SHOWTIME! (pp. 20–21)
Semaphore: What play is it?
Answer: Peter Pan

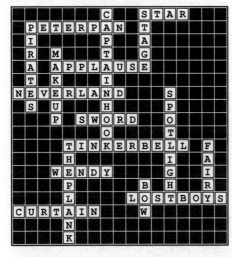

HIKE TO NOWHERE (p. 29)

TIMBER SCOUTS (pp. 30–31)

F	A	T	N
T	N	A	F
N	T	F	A
A	F	N	T

TIME TO RHYME (pp. 32–33)
3. Funny bunny
4. Calm mom
5. Mad dad
6. Crazy daisy
7. Funky monkey
8. Book nook
9. Wrong song
10. Fun run

TEDDY'S ULTIMATE SPORTS TRIVIA (pp. 34–35)
Shaquille O'Neal wears the largest shoes in the NBA. Size 22!
The Tour de France bicycle race lasts 21 days, and Lance Armstrong has won a record 7 times!

FRIENDS FOREVER (p. 38)
Semaphore: Best friends are the best!

DOG DAZE (pp. 40–41)

DOOR-TO-DOOR DISASTERS! (pp. 46–47)

M	S	R	W	C	P
P	W	C	M	R	S
W	C	S	R	P	M
R	P	M	S	W	C
S	R	P	C	M	W
C	M	W	P	S	R

Code: Nate accidentally knocked on Mrs Godfrey's door!

LAUGH RIOT (pp. 50–51)
Q: What do you call a sleeping cow?
A: A bulldozer!
Q: Why did the booger cross the road?
A: Because he was being picked on!

FRANCIS'S CLASSIFIED CODE (pp. 58–59)
Scientists in Peru found a giant penguin
that lived thirty-six million years ago.

ALIAS (pp. 66–67)

G	B	T	P	Q	I	D	A	V
Q	D	A	T	V	B	I	G	P
I	P	V	G	D	A	T	Q	B
B	V	D	I	G	T	A	P	Q
P	I	G	Q	A	V	B	D	T
T	A	Q	D	B	P	G	V	I
D	G	I	V	T	Q	P	B	A
V	T	B	A	P	G	Q	I	D
A	Q	P	B	I	D	V	T	G

YOU ARE THE INVENTOR (p. 71)
Code: This is genius!

BADGE BONANZA
(pp. 60–61)

F	C	H	A
A	H	F	C
H	A	C	F
C	F	A	H

NAME THAT GNOME
(p. 63)
1. Happy
2. Bashful
3. Grumpy
4. Doc
5. Sleepy
6. Dopey
7. Sneezy

SUPER SCOUT CHALLENGE
(pp. 68–69)

FAR-OUT FACTOIDS (pp. 78–79)
Humans have over seven thousand different facial expressions.
In an average lifetime, you will breathe around six hundred million breaths.

**ADVENTURES OF
ULTRA-NATE** (p. 83)
Code: Oh, the suspense!

MAD FOR BADGES
(pp. 85–86)
Codes:
Make some noise!
A shooting star!
Mmm, yum!
Speed demon!

**TOP 5 DOGGONE
FACTS** (p. 94)
2. Ellen
3. Squirrels
4. Go Fish

RHYME-A-THON
(pp. 88–89)
1. New crew
2. King's ring
3. Shy guy
4. Great Nate
5. Pretty kitty
6. Clown's town
7. Grey day
8. Light kite
9. Slow crow
10. Big pig

**DRAMATIC
FLASHBACK**
(pp. 98–99)
Semaphores:
Ouch!
Uh-oh!

CREATE-A-COMIX
(p. 91)
Semaphore: This
should be funny!

SKATER SCRAMBLE
(p. 93)
Semaphore:
If you find more than
fifteen, Nate gets to go to
the skate park!

THE FORTUNE-TELLER (pp. 100–101)
Semaphores:
You will live in the lap of luxury.
You will travel to the moon.
You have a secret admirer.

FACT-TASTIC TRIVIA (pp. 108–109)
A tiglon.
The dodo bird.
The black widow.

PSYCHO DOGS RULE (pp. 114–115)

N	C	T	M	F	G	W	S	P
M	W	F	P	S	N	C	T	G
G	P	S	T	C	W	F	N	M
S	M	C	N	P	T	G	W	F
P	N	G	C	W	F	S	M	T
T	F	W	S	G	M	P	C	N
C	G	M	W	N	P	T	F	S
F	S	N	G	T	C	M	P	W
W	T	P	F	M	S	N	G	C

THE HERO (p. 116)

DESTINED FOR GREATNESS (pp. 126–127)

M	S	C	T
C	T	S	M
T	C	M	S
S	M	T	C

HIDDEN WORDS (p. 137)
Code: If you can make twenty-five words, you earn a whiz kid merit badge!

ZAPPED! (p. 106)

JOKIN' AROUND (pp. 122–123)
Stinkerbell
I'm stuck on you.
The letter "T".

U R CAR2NING! (p. 125)
Semaphore: What's your favourite comic?

THE DOCTOR IS IN! (p. 128)
Code: Is he crazy?

THE GRAND PRIZE (p. 132)

BELIEVE IT OR NOT?
(pp. 138–139)
Venus is the only planet that rotates clockwise.
A duck's quack does not echo.
Most dust particles in your house are made from dead skin.
The elephant is the only mammal that can't jump.

GREAT NATE FACTS
(pp. 140–141)
1. (b) Jenny
2. (c) Skateboard
3. (b) Pulling weeds for Mr. Galvin
4. (a) Maureen Biology.
5. (c) Kevin

SCHOOL PICTURE DAY (p. 155)
Code: Say cheese!

WHO'S A BRAINIAC? (pp. 158–159)
Some turtles can breathe through their butts.
Pearls melt in vinegar.
A butterfly has twelve thousand eyes.

LAUGH-A-THON (p. 160)
A watch dog!
Mice Crispies!
Drop him a line!

EXCLAMATION STATION (pp. 162–163)
Codes: What's wrong with Nate?
Check out Ellen's room!
One scary dude!
Boy, is he mad!

FUNNY BUSINESS (pp. 164–165)
For holding up the pants.
Because they are always stuffed.
The roles weren't good enough.

LOCKER DISASTER (pp. 170–171)

LOTSA LIMERICKS
(p. 149)
Flu
My
Mama
Late
Nate
Doodles
Great

SPORTS SCENE (p. 151)
A diamond
Four
Seven

SAY IT LOUD!
(pp. 152–153)
Codes:
Is Nate in love?
Boring!
Why does Artur look scared?
Coach John explodes!

WHAT COULD GO WRONG?
(p. 161)

WHAT WAS THE QUESTION AGAIN? (pp. 174–175)
Pacific Ocean
Iron and oxygen
The Sahara

HAPPINESS IS . . . WARM FUZZIES (pp. 176–177)

S	U	W	N	L	H	F	G
L	H	F	G	S	U	W	N
U	N	S	W	H	F	G	L
H	G	L	F	U	N	S	W
W	S	H	U	G	L	N	F
N	F	G	L	W	S	U	H
F	W	U	H	N	G	L	S
G	L	N	S	F	W	H	U

ALL MIXED UP! (pp. 182–183)

NATE'S COMIX CRACK-UP (p. 186)

LOST IN THE WOODS (pp. 202–203)

Semaphore: Dad's such a dork!

WHO'S A SPORTS GENIUS?
(pp. 190–191)
Swimming, cycling, and running
Soccer
Badminton
Hop, skip, and jump

CATS AND DOGS (pp. 194–195)

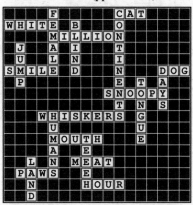

FREAKY FACTS
(pp. 196–197)
Jupiter
Mount Everest
The sun

JUICY GOSSIP
(pp. 198–199)

C	G	R	J
J	R	C	G
G	C	J	R
R	J	G	C

NOTORIOUS NATE TRIVIA
(pp. 200–201)
1. (c) Todd
2. (d) Joe's Hot Dogs
3. (b) Kuddles
4. (d) Randy
5. (c) Pinhead

PRACTICAL JOKESTER (p. 206)
Long time no sea.
Shall we go for a dip?

NATE ≠ NEAT

Have you ever scrambled the letters in your name to see if they spell anything else? Well, **I** have. And guess what: MY letters spell **N·E·A·T!**

Pretty ironic, right? Hey, I realise I'm not exactly Joe Tidy. **EVERYBODY** knows it. But that doesn't stop Francis, who colour-codes his underwear, from pointing it out about a jillion times a day.

Your desk is **DISGUSTING**. You have paint on your shirt. Oh, and you have Cheez Doodle stains near your face. What a SLOB you are!

Francis has been telling me to clean up my act since I poured applesauce down his pants back in kindergarten. Of course, I've always ignored him. But then last week my sloppiness got Francis in trouble... and he **NEVER** gets in trouble!

I felt so bad about it, I decided to actually try to get neater. And thanks to

> I'm **VERY** disappointed in you.

> Oops.

Teddy and his uncle Pedro, the hypnotist, it's working... **TOO** well. All of the sudden, I'm starting to act **JUST LIKE FRANCIS!** Frankly, I think I'm losing my mind.

> You're doing **GREAT!**

> I'm **FLIPPIN' OUT!**

BiG NATE FLIPS OUT

"Big Nate is funny, big time."
—Jeff Kinney, author of Diary of a Wimpy Kid

Lincoln Peirce

What a **MESS!** Read all about it in **BIG NATE FLIPS OUT!!**

Lincoln Peirce

(pronounced "purse") is a cartoonist/writer and author of the *New York Times* bestselling Big Nate series, now published in twenty-five countries. He is also the creator of the comic strip *Big Nate*, which appears in more than 250 U.S. newspapers and online daily at www.bignate.com.

Lincoln loves comics, ice hockey, and Cheez Doodles (and dislikes cats, figure skating, and egg salad). Just like Nate.

Check out Big Nate Island at www.poptropica.com. And link to www.bignatebooks.com for more information about the author and the Big Nate series, app, audio, and ebooks. Lincoln Peirce lives with his wife and two children in Portland, Maine.

BIG NATE FLIPS OUT IS COMING RIGHT UP!